Lolly-Pops

by Bobby Lynn Maslen
pictures by John R. Maslen

Scholastic Inc.

New York • Toronto • London • Auckland • Sydney • Mexico City • New Delhi • Hong Kong • Buenos Aires

Available Bob Books®:

Set 1: Beginning Readers — With consistent new sounds added gradually, your new reader is gently introduced to all the letters of the alphabet. They can soon say, "I read the whole book!®"

Set 2: Advancing Beginners — The use of three-letter words and consistent vowel sounds in slightly longer stories build skill and confidence.

Set 3: Word Families — Consonant blends, endings and a few sight words advance reading skills while the use of word families keep reading manageable.

Set 4: Compound Words — Longer books and complex words engage young readers as proficiency advances.

Set 5: Long Vowels — Silent *e* and other vowel blends build young readers' vocabulary and aptitude.

Bob Books® Collections:

Collection 1 — Includes Set 1: Beginning Readers and part of Set 2: Advancing Beginners

Collection 2 — Includes part of Set 2: Advancing Beginners and Set 3: Word Families

Collection 3 — Includes Set 4: Compound Words and Set 5: Long Vowels

Ask for Bob Books at your local bookstore, or visit www.bobbooks.com.

ISBN 0-545-02689-X

6 5 4 3 2 1   7 8 9 10 11/0

Printed in China
This edition first printing, September 2007

Polly was a jolly bird.

"Hello, Polly," said Jon.
"Hello, Polly," said Dolly.

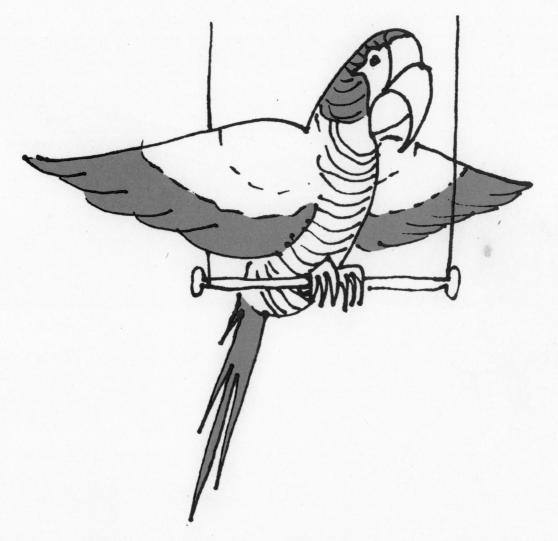

Polly flapped. Polly bobbed.

Polly flew to Dolly.

Polly sat on Dolly.

Dolly and Jon went to a shop.

The shop had lolly-pops.

Jon had six pennies.
Dolly had ten pennies.

Dolly and Jon got lolly-pops.

"Umm, umm, ummm!" said Jon.
"Yum, yum, yum!" said Dolly.

"Awk, awk, awk," said Polly.
"Polly wants a lolly-pop."

"OK," said Dolly.
"Yum, yum!" said Polly.

The End

List of 31 words in <u>Lolly-Pops</u>

<u>Short Vowels</u>

<u>a</u>	<u>e</u>	<u>i</u>	<u>o</u>	<u>u</u>	<u>sight</u>
and	ten	six	on	um	a
had	went		got	yum	to
sat	hello		Jon		OK
flapped	pennies		shop		the
	end		bobbed		awk
			Polly		was
			Dolly		wants
			jolly		bird
			lolly-pop		said
					flew

77 total words in *Lolly-Pops*